Hey

BRING THE CAR AROUND.

YES, SIR!

All right

THE PRESENT'S GOOD TO GO...

rustle

ALL THAT'S LEFT IS...

glance

slide

I DON'T WANNA GO.

WHAT KIND OF MOMMY JUST SLEEPS ALL THE TIME?

SHE'S JUST A STRANGER TO ME...!!

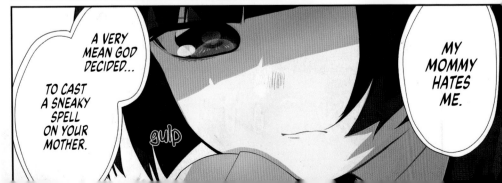

A VERY MEAN GOD DECIDED...

TO CAST A SNEAKY SPELL ON YOUR MOTHER.

MY MOMMY HATES ME.

gulp

YOU SURE YOU GOT EVERYTHING?

LITTLE LADY...

...UH-HUH.

I'M ALL READY.

The Yakuza's Guide to Babysitting

Contents

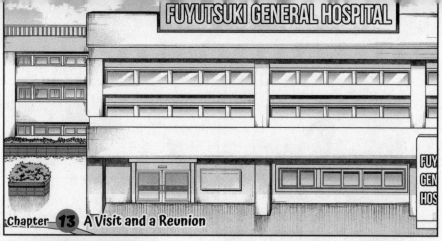

Chapter **13** A Visit and a Reunion

AH!

rattle

I SEE YAE-CHAN'S HERE TODAY TOO.

...UH-HUH.

GREAT, YOU'RE HERE!

GOOD MORNING, EVERYONE!

7

COME ON! LET YOUR MOM SEE YOUR FACE TOO!

THAT MAKES ME REALLY HAPPY.

THANKS FOR COMING.

smile

HEY, BIG SIS.

YAE-CHAN IS HERE TO SEE YOU!

ba-dump

ba-dump

......

MOMMY...

I'M SO
SORRY.

gulp...

I EVEN CALLED YOU A STRANGER AND STUFF...

I'M SORRY.

AND I DIDN'T COME VISIT

YOU'VE BEEN FIGHTING SO HARD ALL THIS TIME...

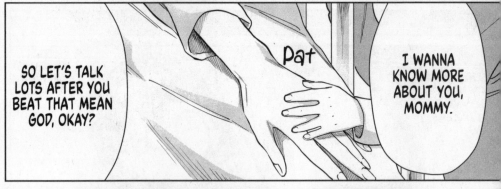

SO LET'S TALK LOTS AFTER YOU BEAT THAT MEAN GOD, OKAY?

Pat

I WANNA KNOW MORE ABOUT YOU, MOMMY.

AND I'LL TELL YOU LOTS ABOUT ME, TOO...

OKAY, MOMMY?

SO PLEASE DON'T GIVE UP.

YIKES, OUR TEAR DUCTS ARE IN TROUBLE.

ha ha

snif

SHE SURE HAS...

What a good girl...

LOOK... YAE-CHAN'S GROWN UP SO MUCH...

Here.

WHAT DID YOU DRAW FOR HER, ANYWAY?

I WANNA BE ABLE TO CHEER HER ON ALL THE TIME...

KIRI-SHIMA...

THE PRESENT...

OH YEAH, GOOD THINKING.

SO I DREW ALL OF US.

...UH-HUH.

NOW YOUR MOM WON'T BE LONELY.

...GOOD IDEA.

WHY DON'T YOU GRAB A SNACK AT THE GIFT SHOP?

WELL, IT IS ALMOST LUNCH-TIME!

SURE, LET'S DO THAT.

Ahaha

GUUUURGL

WUH-OH.

So cute~

IT SEEMS TO ME...

LIKE YAE-CHAN'S GOTTEN USED TO TOORU-KUN.

...MM.

momm

stick

Oh, it's the daifuku sis likes.

EVEN TOORU-KUN'S GOTTEN...

OH, THAT'S RIGHT!

I FEEL LIKE SHE'S MORE TALKATIVE NOW AND SMILES MORE OFTEN.

rustle

to mom

I SAW A FAMILIAR FACE IN THE WAITING ROOM EARLIER!

A FAMILIAR FACE?

PICK OUT WHATEVER YOU WANT.

UH-HUH.

Gift Shop

NOOO!! BUY ME THIS TOOOOO!!!

HOLY CRAP!

KEEP IT DOWN, KID!!

We're in a hospital!

Oof...

FLINCH

hee hee

HE'S CHANGED A LOT SINCE HE WAS IN THE FAMILY,

BUT HE SEEMS TO BE DOING FINE!

?!

BOY, TALK ABOUT A LOUD PAIR OF...

But I've been so good!

Shhh!

peek

URK

THE HOUSE-SITTERS

WE GOT NOTHING ELSE TO DO. WANNA PLAY A GAME?

UHH, SURE...

C'MON, LET'S PLAY OLD MAID.

SUGIHARA-SAN'S NOT EXACTLY A SCARY GUY, IS HE?

whisper

whisper

nod nod

shuff

shuff

OKAY, SO WHOEVER LOSES...

GETS KNEECAPPED BY KIRISHIMA-SAN.

shuff

DAMN, JUST THINKING ABOUT IT GAVE ME GOOSE-BUMPS.

Soo scary!

I TAKE IT ALL BACK.

SHUDDER

badump
badump

Lose and I'm done for...

Chapter **14** Something to Protect

AOI-SAN...?

WAIT...

TOORU?

Ah

...UH, HEY.

MY KIDS ARE GETTING THEIR SHOTS.

Waiting for the younger one now.

WHAT'RE YOU DOING HERE?

I DIDN'T EXPECT TO SEE YOU TOO.

I RAN INTO KANAMI-CHAN EARLIER, BUT...

KIRI-SHIMA... WHO'S THAT?

I GUESS YOU WOULDN'T REMEMBER HIM.

I SAID THE SAME DAMN THING...

ha-ha

DAMN, THOUGH, THE LITTLE MISS HERE'S GOTTEN SO BIG!

DANG, SHE'S CUTE! NOTHING LIKE THE BOSS!

BUT NOW I'M JUST A DAD MYSELF!

THIS IS AOI TOUICHIROU-SAN.

HE USED TO SUPPORT YOUR DAD IN THE SAKURAGI FAMILY.

pat

Hey

WOOOW~

YOU COULDN'T EVEN MAKE A DECENT CUP OF TEA BACK IN THE DAY~

YEAH... GUESS SO.

heh heh

Kanami-chan told me.

YOU'RE THE LITTLE MISS'S BABYSITTER NOW, THOUGH, HUH?

HA HA...

WHAT A DICK...

STARE

I'M GLAD TO HEAR IT, REALLY.

...YEAH. THANK YOU.

STILL, THOUGH.

GUESS YOU'VE GROWN BIG ENOUGH TO FILL MY SHOES...

ha ha

YEAH, HE'S BEEN WRAPPED AROUND HER FINGER SINCE THE DAY SHE WAS BORN.

STILL A DOTING DAD AS ALWAYS.

......

HOW'S THE BOSS?

I CAUSED THE BOSS A LOT OF TROUBLE,

BUT I HAVEN'T MANAGED TO APOLOGIZE PROPERLY YET...

THAT'S MY ONLY REGRET, MAN.

......

GRRR...

YES?

KIRI-SHIMA...

HEY, I TOLD YOU TO SAVE THAT FOR AFTER LUNCH!

It won't open all the way.

DAD, OPEN THIS FOR ME.

C'monnn

Ew, it's covered in spit...

THEY USED TO BE FRIENDS, BUT NOW THEY'RE NOT...?

DID THAT MAN HAVE A FIGHT WITH DADDY?

20

IT'S JUST THAT...

AOI-SAN FOUND...

...THEY'RE STILL VERY GOOD FRIENDS.

THAN WHAT HE WAS PROTECTING WITH YOUR DAD.

SOMETHING EVEN MORE IMPORTANT TO HIM...

AND AOI-SAN COULDN'T PROTECT THAT SPECIAL THING...

IF HE STAYED BY YOUR DAD'S SIDE.

DOES THAT MEAN THEY CAN'T BE FRIENDS ANYMORE?

NO, NOT AT ALL.

SO AOI-SAN HAD TO LEAVE THE FAMILY.

AND AOI-SAN LOVES YOUR DAD, TOO.

YOUR DAD ISN'T MAD AT AOI-SAN...

......

THAT'S GOOD...

OH, OKAY...

Sure

TAKE CARE NOW.

stare...

'KAY.

WE'RE GONNA HEAD OUT.

sanae

All done~

YOU TAKE CARE TOO, LITTLE MISS!

KEEP UP THE GOOD WORK SO THE BOSS DOESN'T KILL YA.

heh

haha...

DON'T SAY SCARY CRAP LIKE THAT, PLEASE.

YOU CAN BE FRIENDS AGAIN.

UM... MY DAD'S...

NOT MAD AT YOU, SO...

...'COURSE NOT...

There, there...

YOU CRYING, DAD?

SNURF

Ah...

LOTTA WEAK TEAR DUCTS AROUND HERE...

LITTLE LADY...

...THANKS, LITTLE MISS.

DO ME A FAVOR AND TELL YOUR DAD...

"I'LL COME VISIT AND BRING YOU A GIFT."

pat

...'KAY.

Ahem

whisper

NO NEED TO LISTEN TO HIM, LITTLE LADY.

Hey, don't leave me out!

SINCE YOU CHEERED ME UP, I'LL TELL YA EMBARRASSING TOORU STORIES.

...SAKURAGI YAEKA.

I'm 7...

HEY.

I'M AOI KOUKI.

I'm 6.

HE DOESN'T MEET A LOTTA KIDS HIS AGE, SO I HOPE THEY GET ALONG.

SO YOUR SON'S A YEAR YOUNGER THAN THE LITTLE LADY.

HOW EXACTLY HAVE YOU BEEN RAISING HIM...?

He plays dirty with the bribes, too...

THAT AIN'T WHAT I MEANT BY "GETTING ALONG", KID!

Don't hit on her!

You can have this.

No thanks...

YOU WANNA GO ON A DATE, YAEKA-CHAN?

Maybe this one would've been better...

Hrmm...

Sakuragi Miyuki

YOU
KNOW,

DEAR...

WHERE'D THAT COME FROM...?

I MEAN, JUST LOOK AT HER!

See?

whisper

I REALLY THINK YAEKA TAKES AFTER YOU.

STARE

"GROUCHY FACE"?

She's mad about something.

THAT GROUCHY FACE LOOKS JUST LIKE YOURS!

AND WHAT WE'LL GET TO DO AS A FAMILY...

I WONDER WHAT SHE'LL GROW UP TO BE LIKE...

YEP, THAT'S THE ONE!

You're making the same face!

DOES IT, THOUGH...?

STARE

THERE'S SO MUCH TO LOOK FORWARD TO.

...OUR LITTLE YAEKA...

IS 7 YEARS OLD NOW.

IT TOOK ME FAR TOO LONG TO SHOW YOU...

HOW MUCH SHE'S GROWN UP...

squeeze

I HAD TO GET HELP FROM A WHOLE LOT OF PEOPLE TO GET THIS FAR.

I HATE TO ADMIT IT, BUT I CAN'T DO A SINGLE DAMN FATHERLY THING ON MY OWN.

THAT RAISING ONE LITTLE GIRL WOULD BE HARDER THAN KEEPING THE WHOLE FAMILY IN LINE.

I HAD NO IDEA...

THAT I BET YOU WOULD'VE EASILY PULLED OFF WITH A SMILE.

I'VE STRUGGLED WITH SO MANY THINGS...

Ah WELCOME BACK~ WHAT TOOK SO LONG?

HEY, WE'RE BACK.

RATTLE

TOTTER

UM, DADDY?

THAT AOI PERSON SAID...

OH, SO YOU SAW HIM TOO~

Thanks~

I picked up some drinks.

WE RAN INTO AOI-SAN AND CHATTED FOR A BIT.

RUSTLE

"I'LL COME VISIT AND BRING YOU A GIFT."

...I SEE.

HE ASKED ME TO TELL YOU.

OOF... IT'S SUPER OBVIOUS WHAT HE'S THINKING...

Like an open book...

SAY IT TO MY FACE, YOU BASTARD

UH-HUH.

MESSAGE RECEIVED. THANK YOU.

HE SEEMED TO FEEL GUILTY ABOUT LEAVING THE FAMILY.

DID AOI-KUN SAY ANY-THING?

WHEN AOI-KUN LEFT THE FAMILY...

YOU WERE A LITTLE SAD, WEREN'T YOU, TOORU-KUN?

I GUESS HE HASN'T CHANGED A BIT.

THAT GUY'S ALWAYS PUTTING OTHER PEOPLE BEFORE HIMSELF.

BUT...

WHETHER THAT'S HOW HE REALLY FEELS OR NOT...

HE ACTS LIKE IT'S SO OBVIOUS...

WHY? I GOT PROMOTED TO RIGHT-HAND MAN. I WAS PSYCHED.

I... I SEE...

YOU SENT THE OTHER GUYS TO THE FREAKIN' HOSPITAL!

It hurts.

BUT. LOOK. I GOT HIT TOO.

Don't give me that!

YOU WENT OFF THE DAMN CHAIN AGAIN, DIDN'T YA...?!

HEY, TOORU...

GRRRRR

We're gonna go settle this.

GET OVER HERE!!

THAT GROUP'S A PAIN IN THE ASS WHEN YOU MESS WITH 'EM...

He always comes home injured.

Isn't this a rerun from last week...?

I called their bluff...

WELL, THEY TOLD ME TO GO AHEAD AND TRY, SO...

THESE DAYS, TOORU-KUN'S APPROACH TO LIFE DEFINITELY REFLECTS AOI-KUN'S.

TOORU-KUN WAS ALWAYS RIGHT BEHIND AOI-KUN...

I BET HE'S MODELING HIMSELF AFTER AOI-KUN WITHOUT EVEN REALIZING IT.

hee hee

SURE THING.

WE SHOULD HEAD HOME.

Take care

34

MOMMY...

snff

THE LITTLE LADY...

......

I'LL COME AGAIN SOON.

to mommy

SHALL WE GO NOW,

LITTLE LADY?

WHY DO YOU REMEMBER THAT...?

UH-HUH...

ONE TIME WHEN HE GOT REALLY MAD AT YOU BACK IN THE DAY...

RUNNING INTO AOI-KUN REMINDED ME.

UNLIKE CANNON-BALLS, I ALWAYS COME BACK, SO...

I'M MORE LIKE A BOOMER-ANG.

WOULD YOU QUIT GOING THROUGH LIFE LIKE A DAMN LOOSE CANNON?

AND THEN YOU ANSWERED...

SERIOUSLY, WHY WOULD YOU HANG ON TO THAT MEMORY...?

You were the only one laughing at the time.

With a straight face, too...

I THOUGHT IT WAS SO FUNNY THAT YOU'D MAKE SUCH A BAD JOKE(?)...

bonk

Ow.

Don't say such stupid BS.

Chapter **16** Ohagi's Big Day

OHAGI WANTS FOOD...

trot

trot

RATTLE...

Meooow~

Mew!

Myaaa~

tmp

rrrub

RATTLE

WAS THAT SUPPOSED TO MEAN "GOOD MORNING"...?

clatter
clatter
clatter

swish

She's not here...

HUH?

YOUR FOOD...

OHAGI.

blink

trot

trot

DAMN, IT'S PACKED... IS THIS ALL THE BOSS'S STUFF?

Rrrawr...

GUESS WE'LL JUST MOVE 'EM ONE AT A...

hup

RUSTLE

GWAH?!

WHUMP

WHUMP

WHUMP

HSAARC

WAH?!

CLUTTER

THUMP
THUMP
THUMP
THUMP
THUMP
THUMP
THUMP

WHAT THE HELL HAPPENED HERE?

URGH...

I-I'M SORRY...

YEAH, IT'S PROBABLY STILL IN THIS ROOM...

BLACK THING

Eep

A BLACK THING?

THE BOSS ASKED US TO SORT THROUGH SOME ANTIQUES...

BUT THERE WAS A BLACK THING IN THERE...

KIRI-SHIMA...?

Oh

MORNING, LITTLE LADY.

YIKES!

AND IT GROWLED, TOO.

NO, WAY BIGGER...

WHAT KINDA BLACK THING? LIKE A COCKROACH?

BONK

hop

?!!

OHAGI WANTED HER FOOD...

OHAGI?

IS SOMETHING THE MATTER?

!

bonk bonk

I SEE... I WONDER WHERE SHE COULD'VE GONE.

SHE WOKE ME UP, SO I WENT TO FEED HER, BUT I CAN'T FIND HER.

~ having flashbacks ~

Meoooow Meoooow

WAAAH...

Get meowt of here...

Mrrow...

MYAAAAAAAOW!

WHA?!

...WAIT, HUH?!

IT WAS COMING FROM OVER HERE...

WAS THAT OHAGI'S MEOW...?!

YOU JUST REALIZED THIS NOW?

What "monster vision"?

My monster vision went into overdrive...

COULD THAT BLACK THING HAVE BEEN OHAGI...?!

HER VOICE IS GETTING QUIETER...

pop

SHE MUST BE IN HERE SOMEWHERE, THOUGH...

Myow...

Mrrrow...

skrtch skrtch skrtch

WE'LL JUST HAVE TO SEARCH 'EM ONE BY ONE!

SHUFF

R-RIGHT...!

MY INTERNAL ORGANS SHOULD BE ENOUGH TO PAY FOR THIS, RIGHT...?

BRO KE

CALM DOWN, TAKEUCHI.

DID YOU FIND HER?!

AH?!

P
O
P

AH!

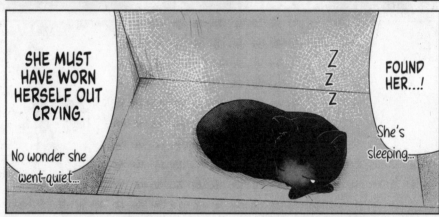

SHE MUST HAVE WORN HERSELF OUT CRYING.

No wonder she went quiet...

Z
Z
Z

FOUND HER...!

She's sleeping...

And they all lived happily ever after...

BUT DON'T RUN OFF BY YOURSELF, OKAY?

I'M SORRY. I SHOULDN'T HAVE TAKEN MY EYES OFF YOU...!

UH...

Mew...

shff

KIRI-SHIMA-SAN...!

C'MON, DON'T WORRY SO MUCH.

THE BOSS IS HUMAN TOO.

GLOOOOOOM

OH, RIGHT.

I WOULDN'T SAY ALL OF US...

S

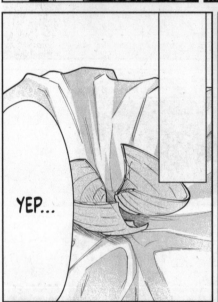

YEP...

I'M SURE HE'LL SETTLE FOR YOUR ORGANS.

THAT'S NOT HELPFUL!

bright smile

HOW DO YOU PLAN TO...

Meeeow~

HE WAS DEAD ON!

urgh

BOTH YOUR ORGANS SHOULD JUST ABOUT COVER THIS.

BAM

Mew!

Myaaaa~

I'M THE ONE WHO SCARED THOSE TWO...!

SO PLEASE DON'T GET MAD AT THEM...!

Little lady?!

SHE'S INTERPRET-ING?!

......

Mrrow...

slump...

THE TWO OF THEM FED OHAGI FANCY TREATS FOR A WHILE.

YES, SIR! WE'RE SO SORRY!

Lost the will to get angry

DON'T LET IT HAPPEN AGAIN...

sigh

FWIP

WHY DOES OHAGI...

SEEM TO LIKE EVERYONE BUT ME...?

HIERAR-CHY...?

THEY SAY CATS HAVE THEIR OWN HIERARCHY, RIGHT?

Ow!

RARR

swipe

THE OTHER DAY, SHE BEAT THE CRAP OUT OF ME JUST FOR WALKING BY...

I'M LOWER THAN FOOD?!

SO OHAGI'S HIERARCHY PROBABLY LOOKS LIKE THIS.

Come onnn...

KEEP AN EYE ON THE HOUSE FOR US.

wave

SEE YOU LATER, LITTLE LADY.

wave

Chapter 17 Operation: Befriend the Little Lady

YES, SIR!

WE'LL BE WAITING FOR YA!

HAVE A NICE DAY.

Myaaa~

I'LL BE SPENDING THE DAY WITH THE LITTLE LADY.

I GUESS THAT MEANS...

glance

stare

THERE'S ONE THING I'VE GOT TO DO BEFORE THEN...

IT'LL BE ABOUT 5 HOURS BEFORE KIRISHIMA-SAN AND THE BOSS GET BACK FROM THEIR MEETING.

ONCE AND FOR ALL!

You'll get your food soon.

Mew

"MAKE FRIENDS WITH THE LITTLE LADY."

I DON'T THINK SHE'S EVER GOTTEN TO KNOW ME AS A PERSON.

Sugihara

Sugihara

ALL THIS TIME, I'VE JUST BEEN A VAGUE PRESENCE NEXT TO KIRISHIMA-SAN, BUT...

THAT'S THE LAST THING I WANT! I CAN'T TAKE IT!

AT THIS RATE, I'LL STAY AS "THE GUY WHO HANGS OUT WITH KIRISHIMA" FOREVER!

* THIS MAN IS IN THE YAKUZA

BANG

NOW'S MY CHANCE, WHILE KIRISHIMA-SAN AND THE BOSS AREN'T AROUND!

?!!

SHOOM

FLINCH

LITTLE LADY!

I'LL BEFRIEND HER IF IT'S THE LAST THING I DO!!

YA MIND IF I EAT NEXT TO YOU TODAY?!

WAH

* SERIOUSLY, HE'S IN THE YAKUZA

WE'RE BOUND TO STRIKE UP CONVERSATION AND GET TO KNOW EACH OTHER!

BY SHARING A MEAL AND SPENDING TIME TOGETHER...

clench

...?

'KAY...

THANK YA!

blink

clack

clack

IT'S DEAD QUIET.

NOPE.

Slurp

52

HAS ANYTHING FUN HAPPENED AT SCHOOL LATELY?

LITTLE LADY!

NO, WAIT. THE LITTLE LADY DOESN'T TALK MUCH TO BEGIN WITH...

SO I'LL JUST HAVE TO GET THE BALL ROLLING!

gloom

...I DON'T REALLY HAVE FRIENDS...

NOW I'VE DONE IT!

Hrmm

...NOT REALLY.

UH... LIKE PLAYING WITH FRIENDS, OR...

WHAT WOULD KIRISHIMA-SAN DO RIGHT NOW...

hmm

hmm...

AND OF COURSE IT HAD TO BE KANEHIRA ON MEAL DUTY TODAY, AND HE'S NO DAMN HELP...

Say something, dude!

swoosh swoosh

LITTLE LADY!

fwip

YOU'VE GOTTA GET THROUGH THIS ON YOUR OWN...!

GAAAAAAAH

NO, DON'T FALL BACK ON HIM!!

Aah

ONCE WE'RE DONE EATING, WANT TO SEE MY ROOM?!

lick
lick

THESE ARE ALL MOVIES?

WOW, SO MANY...!

Yep!

YOU CAN PICK WHATEVER YOU'D LIKE!

Ta-daaaa

I'VE SEEN ALL OF THESE, AND I HAVE KIDS' MOVIES, TOO.

heh heh

OKAY, THIS ONE...

shff...

Movie
Mii-chan and the Magic Manor

OH, THE MII-CHAN SERIES!

I'M SURE THE LITTLE LADY WILL ENJOY THIS...!

vreeee

IF WE CAN ENJOY THIS TOGETHER, WE'LL BE FRIENDS FOR SURE!

with carrots!

She powers up

THE KINDLY RABBIT GIRL MII-CHAN

IT'S SUPER FAMOUS, AND I HAVE THE WHOLE SERIES!!

PERFECT! THIS ONE'S A FANTASY ANIME FOR KIDS AND ADULTS ALIKE!

the end

sniffle

snuffl

sniff

3 HOURS LATER

I FORGOT THIS ONE'S A TEARJERKER.

GUH— HUH...

SNORF

ARE YOU OKAY...?

THE LITTLE LADY LOOKS KINDA WEIRDED OUT, TOO...

Here's some tissues...

I GOT EVEN MORE INVESTED THAN HER AND BAWLED LIKE A DAMN BABY...!

INSTEAD OF ENJOYING IT TO-GETHER...

perk

YOU WATCH MOVIES WITH KIRISHIMA?

KIRISHIMA-SAN ALWAYS SMACKS ME AND TELLS ME TO "CAN IT" WHEN WE WATCH MOVIES TOGETHER...

PHOOO

SORRY, LITTLE LADY... I'M ALWAYS LIKE THIS, I'M AFRAID.

Oh, yeah.

MOSTLY, HE JUST KINDA SHOWS UP PARTWAY THROUGH, BUT...

HE GETS BORED PRETTY EASILY,

SO HE ONLY HAS PATIENCE FOR SELF-CONTAINED STORIES LIKE MOVIES...

OH, WOW...

HUH...

AS SOON AS THE TOPIC OF KIRISHIMA-SAN CAME UP, SHE STARTED ENJOYING HERSELF...?

Ack

SHE'S THAT MUCH CLOSER WITH KIRISHIMA-SAN THAN ME...?!

DOES THIS MEAN...

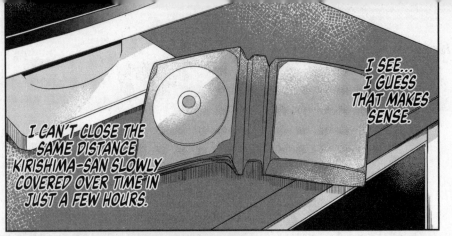

I SEE... I GUESS THAT MAKES SENSE.

I CAN'T CLOSE THE SAME DISTANCE KIRISHIMA-SAN SLOWLY COVERED OVER TIME IN JUST A FEW HOURS.

LITTLE LADY...

WHICH MEANS I'VE ONLY GOT ONE OPTION LEFT HERE...

A FEW DAYS LATER

KIRI- SHIMA...

I'LL TELL YOU WHATEVER YOU WANT TO KNOW ABOUT KIRISHIMA-SAN!

HE'LL USE WHATEVER ADVANTAGES HE CAN GET

YES! I WAS GLAD I GOT TO TALK TO HER PROPERLY—

SLAM

HEY, DIDJA HAVE FUN WATCHING THE HOUSE WITH THE LITTLE LADY?

Eeeek

s·m·i·i·i·l·e

HIS FACE DOESN'T MATCH HIS WORDS AT ALL!

UNLESS YOU LIKE SLEEPING WITH ONE EYE OPEN.

DON'T GO BLABBING ANY MORE SECRETS TO HER...

Ah—

A FEW SECONDS LATER, HE GOT PUNCHED FOR REAL.

OR WAS IT PUDDING, NOT ICE CREAM?!

ba—dump

ba—dump

WHAT'S HE SO MAD ABOUT ....?

crumble

Whoa, I didn't know walls broke this easily...

Happy Valentine's Day!!

GOSH, THERE'S SO MANY OPTIONS TO CHOOSE FROM~

SAMPLE

...'KAY.

SO WE'LL MAKE WHATEVER YOU WANT!

THIS'LL BE YOUR FIRST TIME MAKING CHOCOLATES FROM SCRATCH...

heh heh

I FIGURED IT OUT WITH SURVEY-LENS.

DID TOORU-KUN TELL YOU THAT?

Han

SO I WANNA MAKE IT REALLY CHOCO-LATE-Y.

KIRI-SHIMA LIKES CHOCO-LATE,

SURVEIL-LANCE?!

Chapter 18 Our First Valentine's Day

THANKS FOR HAVIN' ME.

Hello~

crunch

crunch

WELCOME HO...

I FIGURED I'D INVITE HER OVER!

THIS IS THE GIRL WHO FOUND OHAGI-CHAN, RIGHT?

Ah...?

SHE'S WITH US, TOORU-KUN!

Don't throw her out!

toss

clatter

SCUSE ME, WE'VE GOT AN INTRUD-ER...

Ahhh

Ohagi-chan...

YOU GAVE THE KITTY A PRETTY TASTY-SOUNDING NAME, HUH?

droo!

IS FOOD ALL YOU THINK ABOUT, KID?

UH-HUH...

YOU KNOW THIS IS A YAKUZA HOUSE, RIGHT...?

Ah

BUT WE'RE HAVING A GIRLS' NIGHT NOW, SO YOU'RE NOT ALLOWED.

GOD, SHE SUCKS.

DON'T CALL ME THAT, WEIRDO.

twitch...

IT'S NICE TO SEE YOU AGAIN, TOORU-KUN-SAN.

Heya

COME ON, WE'RE BUDDIES, AREN'T WE?

AYUMU-CHAN, YOU WERE IN THE VALENTINE'S SECTION EARLIER...

Pancake Mix

soft n' fluffy~!

Oh

I was just there to eat 'em.

IS THAT RIGHT...

NAH.

THAT SHOP GIVES OUT CHOCOLATE SAMPLES EVERY YEAR.

GURGL

Cocoa Powder

DO YOU HAVE A CRUSH AT SCHOOL?

BUT THIS IS YOUR FIRST YEAR, RIGHT, YAE-CHAN?

I DO WHEN I HAVE TIME~

SO, D'YOU LADIES... MAKE CHOCOLATE EVERY YEAR?

UH-HUH.

......

I'M GONNA GIVE KIRISHIMA SOME.

SO YOU LIKE SOMEONE OR WHAT?

AWW~

AND DADDY AND HIS FRIENDS, TOO.

HOW CUTE!

HMM?

...MAN, THIS KINDA THING IS NICE.

I'VE NEVER HAD A CRUSH OR ANYTHING, SO...

THAT YOU GET TO FEEL ALL MUSHY INSIDE AND STUFF.

I'M KINDA JEALOUS...

Mushy...

HER STOMACH'S BEEN GROWLING NONSTOP...

GUUUUUURGL

NOT THAT I MIND, SINCE I'D RATHER HAVE FOOD.

66

WHAT, DID THE SMELL OF CAKE ATTRACT YOU?

hee hee

GRRR

WE'RE NOT ALL LIKE YOU, DUMBASS.

TOORU-KUN! IS EVERYONE OVER IN THE OFFICE?

YEP.

YES, LITTLE LADY?

KIRI-SHIMA...

tmp tmp

HEY, GUYS! COME TRY THE CAKE WE JUST MADE~!

OH?

YOU BAKED THIS YOUR-SELF?

I MADE CHOCOLATE CAKE.

HERE, THESE ARE FOR YOU.

shff...

!

IT'S DELICIOUS!

SHIINE

OMPH

I ADDED EXTRA CHOCOLATE TO YOURS.

It's crunchy.

THERE'S LOTS OF CHOCOLATE CHIPS IN HERE, HUH?

AWW, YOU DID?

BUT DON'T TELL THE OTHERS, 'KAY?

'CAUSE I KNOW YOU LIKE CHOCOLATE...

Shhh

...ALL RIGHT, IT'S OUR SECRET.

Shh

So blinding... wow...

TALK ABOUT HEART-WARMING...

HEE HEE...

THANK YOU VERY MUCH.

I'M HUNGRY. GUESS I'LL GO HOME AND EAT MY...

WH UMP

I GUESS I'LL NEVER BE LIKE THAT...

LOOM

wobble OOF...

SORRY.
MY BA...

HE'S HUGE.

AH...
My cake...

paff

GRAB

?!

nod

THANKS VERY MUCH...

blink

I MUST DROPPE IT WHEN CRASHE INTO HIM...

HEY, MISTER.

?!

GRAB

BA-DUMP

....?!

?!

I'M NOT GONNA FORGET YOU.

sparkle

YOU MADE MY HEART SKIP A BEAT FOR THE FIRST TIME...

sparkle

sparkle

HANG IN THERE, KANEHIRA...

Oh dear

DID WE JUST SEE SOMEONE FALL IN LOVE...?

?

I EVEN HAD A NICE LITTLE MEET-CUTE...

Ah

munch munch

munch

THAT WAS A PRETTY GREAT VALENTINE'S DAY.

Ingredients: Pancake Mix

sparkle

sparkle

sparkle

THIS CAKE LED ME TO THAT GUY. IT'S BASICALLY THE CAKE OF LOVE (?)...

WHEN I PUT IT THAT WAY, IT'S ALMOST A SHAME TO EAT IT...

gaah...

I ATE IT ALL.

I SHOULD AT LEAST TAKE A PICTURE.

nom

Where's my phone...

Mister...

Kazematei Lodge

Chapter **19** Demon

SLOUCH

UUUGH...

I'M BEAT...

Break Room

YO.

YOU'RE KIRISHIMA, YEAH?

I hear you're babysitting now?

ALMOST EVERYONE AT THE BOSS'S DAMN MEETING HAD TO GIVE ME THEIR TWO CENTS.

How many times do I have to hear that one?

...HUH?

WHO THE HELL'RE YOU?

HAVING FUN BABYSITTING FOR A LITTLE GIRLIE?

THIS PUNK...!

GRRRR

HELLO? OH, LITTLE LADY?

VRRRRRR

beep

I'M FROM THE KUSAGAMI FAMILY. NAME'S YANAGI—

RIGHT, GUESS I DIDN'T INTRODUCE MYSELF.

LAUGHING LIKE A DAMN FOOL.

tch

"DEMON OF SAKURAGI" MY ASS...

YES, I THINK WE'LL BE DONE SOON.

IF THERE'S ANYTHING YOU'D LIKE, I'LL PICK IT UP ON THE WAY HOME.

beep

GUESS IT'S TRUE WHAT THEY SAY.

YOU'RE JUST A GOOD LITTLE BABYSITTER NOW, HUH...?

THAT OLD MAN OF YOURS REALLY GOT YOU SO SCARED?

feh

THE HELL...? HIS WHOLE VIBE JUST CHANGED....!

SHIVER

!

...YOU SURE LIKE TO RUN YOUR MOUTH, PAL.

phooo

WHAT I'M DOING AIN'T "BABYSITTING", SEE?

IT'S A JOB.

FWUMP

I AIN'T GONNA BABYSIT YOUR CORPSE, GOT IT?

DON'T TALK BIG WHEN YOU DON'T KNOW SHIT.

....!

gulp...

IF THAT WERE THE OLD KIRISHIMA, YOU'D BE DEAD NOW, YANAGI.

HUNH?!

EVEN IF HE'S SOFTENED UP, I WOULDN'T MESS WITH HIM.

YOU GOT NO IDEA HOW OFTEN I'VE BEEN GLAD WE'RE ON THE SAME SIDE...

IF HE'S NOT GONNA MAKE A MOVE, THEN WE GOTTA DO IT INSTEAD...!

...SEE, IT'S 'CAUSE OF THIS SHIT THAT PEOPLE LOOK DOWN ON US.

SO THIS IS MII-CHAN?

Nope.

sniff

THAT'S RABI-KUN.

LET'S SEE HERE...

I'M NOT GOOD WITH NAMES AND STUFF...

SORRY 'BOUT THAT.

Haha...

YOU ALWAYS GET THEM MIXED UP.

Mrr

KIRISHIMA.

WHO'S THIS?

......

stare

THAT'S, UH...

RABI-KUN?

No!

IT'S MII-CHAN!

NOW THIS PLACE'S IN THE KUSAGAMI CASH BOX.

HE GAVE IN AFTER TWO OR THREE PUNCHES.

THAT MANAGER WAS A JOKE.

CHATTER

CHATTER

Seventee

ha ha ha

NAH, HE WON'T COME.

HE'S PROBABLY PLAYING HOUSE WITH THE LITTLE GIRLIE RIGHT NOW.

HYUK HYUK

YOU SURE ABOUT THIS, BRO? WE'RE ON SAKURAGI TURF.

IF THAT KIRISHIMA GUY SHOWS UP...

CHATTER CHATTER

Wahaha

CHATTER

BESIDES, THE "DEMON OF SAKURAGI" AIN'T ALL THAT.

THOSE WUSSES FROM THE OTHER FAMILIES TAKE HIM TOO SERIOUSLY.

CHATTER

Ahaha for real?

CHATTER

IN THE END, HE'S JUST A...

SAY IT TO MY FACE, WHY DON'TCHA?

...YO.

THUNK

SHOULDN'T YOU BE BABYSITTING RIGHT NOW—

CLATTER

K...

KIRISHI-MA...?!

TRY TO KEEP UP, PAL...

...OUR LITTLE LADY IS VERY WELL-BEHAVED.

YOU COULD LEARN A THING OR TWO FROM HER.

WHAT... THE HELL ...?!

ARE S'POSED TO BE IN BED BY NOW.

GOOD LITTLE BOYS AND GIRLS

SPLASH

BACK OFF! WHO THE HELL DO Y...

THIS GUY'S BAD NEWS...!

SHUDDER

HRMM?

YOU LOOK KINDA HAPPY...

THE NEXT DAY

KIRISHIMA...

DID SOME-THING GOOD HAPPEN?

WAS IT THAT OBVIOUS?

OH, SILLY ME.

I HAD A BIT OF FUN YESTERDAY...

Ha ha

SO I WAS JUST LAUGHING ABOUT IT A LITTLE.

Brooo! You gotta wake up!

diiiing

......

shff

Hrmm

I SAID I'D BURY 'EM, BUT IT'LL BE A PAIN TO DIG THE HOLES...

Aaaaaaaaaargh!

I COME RUNNING FOR AN "EMERGENCY", AND YOU TELL ME TO DIG HOLES?!

COME ON, KIRISHIMA-SAN!

HE ALWAYS WORKS FASTER WHEN HE'S HALF-ASLEEP...

He's twice as whiny, though.

PUT YOURSELF IN MY SHOES FOR ONCE!

Who are these guys, anyway?

It's cold! I'm tired!

I JUST WOKE UP, AND I'VE GOTTA DIG 6 FEET DEEP...

A man who usually calls in favors around 2~3 AM

Whoa!

OH MAN!

Hff...

Chapter **20** Good to See You Again

THIS PLACE IS HUGE!

...HERE GOES.

Phew...

LATELY HE WANTS TO TAG ALONG WHEREVER I GO.

Yeah...

YOU CAME TO VISIT TOO, KOUKI-KUN?

Welcome~

Hullo!

'SCUSE ME, I'M HERE!

RATTLE

I CAME TO SEE YOUR DAD.

...UH-HUH.

...HEY, LITTLE MISS.

Right this way

OK 'PRECIATE IT.

Take your time~

ALL RIGHT, I'LL KEEP AN EYE ON THE KIDS.

Yaeka-chan, let's plaaay!!

patter

YOU GOT HERE 20 MINUTES EARLY...

'CAUSE YOU NEEDED TIME TO WORK UP THE NERVE TO WALK IN, RIGHT?

'SCUSE ME?

...SO, YOU SEEM PRETTY NERVOUS.

Ha ha ha ha

NO, YOU'RE JUST VERY EASY TO READ, AOI-SAN.

WHAT WAS THAT?!

...YOU ALWAYS WERE A LITTLE TOO GOOD AT READING PEOPLE...

YOU DON'T HAVE...

A SINGLE THING TO WORRY ABOUT.

...IT'LL BE FINE.

GOOD TO SEE YOU AGAIN...

AOI.

Heh

DON'T COME IN HERE LOOKING LIKE A DAMN WIMP.

IT'S GOOD TO SEE YOU TOO... BOSS...!

...

...YEAH.

...THE HELL ARE YOU CRYING FOR?

I-

I'M NOT CRYING!

tp

THEY CAUGHT ME UP A BIT AT THE HOSPITAL...

SO THE MISSUS'S CONDITION HASN'T CHANGED AT ALL, THEN?

...YEP.

OH, YEAH, THANKS FOR ASKING! SANAE'S DOING GREAT!

WHAT ABOUT YOUR WIFE? SHE FEELING ANY BETTER?

YOU KNOW, BOSS...

I'VE BEEN MEANING TO THANK YOU ALL THIS TIME.

You have the gifts, right? Tell them I said hello!

I know, I know

Stop asking us already!!

THAT RIGHT...

SHE KEPT GOING ON ABOUT GIFTS AND THANK-YOUS.

WHEN I TOLD HER I WAS COMING HERE TO VISIT TODAY,

THE FAMILY I REALLY NEEDED TO PROTECT WAS MY OWN...

THAT REALLY OPENED MY EYES.

I CAN HOLD MY HEAD UP HIGH AND SAY THAT I'M TRULY HAPPY.

AND NOW WE'RE BLESSED WITH TWO KIDS.

ONCE I LEFT, SANAE'S CONDITION STABILIZED...

SO THANK YOU, BOSS...

FROM THE BOTTOM OF MY HEART...!

AOI-SAN BOWING HIS HEAD TO THE BOSS...

I SAW THIS SAME SCENE WHEN HE LEFT THE FAMILY.

BOTH OF THEM...

BUT IT AIN'T THE SAME AT ALL.

LOOK A HELL OF A LOT HAPPIER THIS TIME AROUND.

Yaeka-chan, you're good~

GOTTA SAY, IT FEELS WEIRD.

...WELL, HOW ABOUT THAT.

BUT NOW I GET TO SEE KOUKI HANGING OUT WITH THE LITTLE MISS.

I DIDN'T THINK I'D EVER SET FOOT IN THIS HOUSE AGAIN...

AND YOU, TOORU...

ALL 'CAUSE THE LITTLE MISS INVITED ME AT THE HOSPITAL.

I'M REALLY GLAD I CAME TODAY.

shiiiiiiiiine

LOOK! I DID GOOD!

KOUKI...

STOMP STOMP STOMP

SINCE I LEFT THE FAMILY, YOU...

HEY, DAAAD!!

LOOK, I'M HAVING AN IMPORTANT TALK HERE...

OH?

What IS this..?

Puff

Puff

ISN'T IT GREAT?!

WHEN I LEFT THE FAMILY...

Ooh

WOW, VERY NICE.

IT'S OHAGI SITTING.

Let me see.

YOU DREW SOMETHING TOO, LITTLE LADY?

YOU WERE BEING CALLED "DEMON", AND I FELT LIKE I'D LET YOU LOOSE...

I'VE BEEN WORRIED ABOUT THAT ALL THIS TIME.

?

?

WEREN'T YOU SAYING SOME-THING?

AOI-SAN?

BUT NOW...

Ah

...NAH.

LOOKS LIKE I WAS WORRIED FOR NOTHING.

FORGET ABOUT IT.

Heh

??

Hm?

I THOUGHT YOU WEREN'T A FAN OF SWEETS?

RUSSL

RUSSL

OH, THAT'S RIGHT. WE BROUGHT A GIFT FROM OUR FAVORITE CAKE SHOP.

C'monnn

DAD, AREN'T WE GONNA EAT THAT CAKE?

I BUY 'EM FOR HER ALL THE TIME WHEN WE'VE HAD A FIGHT...

Urk

I DON'T EAT 'EM, BUT SANAE LOVES THE STUFF.

A MAKE-UP CAKE...

QUIT REPEATING THAT!

MAKE-UP CAKE...

IT'S A MAKE-UP CAKE.

Ughh

...FORGET I SAID THAT.

make-up cake

YOU CAN'T GO TO THE PARK, KIRISHIMA?

SO WE'LL HAVE TO DO THE PARK SOME OTHER...

I'M SORRY.

AN IMPORTANT ERRAND JUST CAME UP...

AND SOOO...

READY TO GO

Ahh...

I CAN'T DO IT...

WE'LL BE ACCOMPANYING YOU IN KIRISHIMA-SAN'S PLACE!

TA-DAAAAAAAA!

OKAY.

Oh

HE'S A MESS ON HIS OWN, SO YOU GO TOO.

pat

POOR SUGI-HARA-SAN...

LET'S GO TO THE PARK!

I still get to go!

Chapter **21** My First Friend

SO, LITTLE LADY...

Fuyutsuki Park

THAT
OUGHTA
DO IT...

WHAT
SHALL WE
DO?

YOU
BROUGHT
A FEW
THINGS,
RIGHT?

JUMP
ROPES, A
BUCKET,
AND A
SHOVEL.

WE COULD
MAKE ONE
LONG JUMP
ROPE?
Since
there's 2

YEAH!

ONE,
TWO...

sparkle

sparkle

sparkle

FWIP

ALL
RIGHT,
HERE
GOES!

Who's that?!

Yaaay

blink

SARA... CHAN?

IS SHE A FOREIGNER, MAYBE?

sparkle

WANNA PLAY JUMP ROPE!

MY NAME IS SARA!

sparkle

sparkle

YAEKA!

SAKURAGI YAEKA...

Um

WHAT'S YOUR NAME?

Ooone...

twooo...

threee...

OKAY, THEN...

ONE, TWO—

WOW, NO PRESSURE...

JUMP ROPE! LET'S PLAY! JUMP ROPE! WANNA PLAY!

shake

shake

WHEE

YAEKA IS THE BEST!

WOW! 30 WHOLE TIMES!

THWAP

30!

YOU CAN DO WHATEVER YOU WANT, LITTLE LADY!

Whew

UMM...

They're all tangled...

Umm...

sparkle

sparkle

I WANNA PLAY WITH YOU MORE!

WHAT NEXT, WHAT NEXT?

sparkle

!

tug

YAEKA!

!

OH, YES!

Umm...

OKAY, THEN... MAYBE THE SWINGS?

....!

LET'S GO!

UH-HUH...

Yeah!! Whoa

flinch

CLANG CLANG

Up you go!

Eeek!

Aah

splut

!! !!

KA- POP

badump badump

Aww!

Ah

PAPA!

Hey!

SARAAA!

...UH-HUH!

WHY'S SUGIHARA-SAN CRYING...?

HUH? UH, YEAH...

sniffle

THE LITTLE LADY MADE A FRIEND, TAKEUCHI...!

THE NEXT DAY

HELLO, WE JUST MOVED IN NEXT DOOR!

I am Leon, and she is Sara!

YAEKA! YOU LIVE CLOSE!

Huh?!

YOU'RE OUR NEW NEIGHBORS?!

BAAAAAAM!

Let's play!

WHAT? HOW COME?

Whew

IT'S A GOOD THING KIRISHIMA-SAN DIDN'T GO TO THE PARK, Y'KNOW?

G-GOOD POINT...

NO ONE WOULD COME NEAR THAT, LET ALONE SARA-CHAN.

Heh heh, now isn't that fun?

Like the kind that'd zap you.

IF HE WAS THE ONE HOLDING THE JUMP ROPE, IT'D LOOK LIKE A WEAPON.

❖MENTAL IMAGE

THEY BOTH BECAME SACRIFICES.

ACK

FWIP

SO ONE OF US WOULD HAVE TO BE A SACRIFI...

BUT ONE PERSON CAN'T TURN A JUMP ROPE...

Seriously...

Man, that was a beating...

A GIFT FOR THE LITTLE LADY'S BIRTHDAY?

Chapter **22** The Best Present

WELL, AIN'T THAT NICE. WHEN IS HER BIRTHDAY, ANYWAY?

IT'S APRIL 11TH!

The day after next!

OF COURSE! SHE'S IN SECOND GRADE NOW, SO I MADE HER A NEW HANDBAG!

...HM?

?

?

Wait...

WE CELEBRATE HER BIRTHDAY HERE EVERY YEAR, REMEMBER?

DO WE REALLY?

News to me.

hup

C'MON... THAT MAKES ME SOUND LIKE A PSYCHO... I'm not that bad...

You were off someplace last year, too.

Oh, I see! YOU MUST'VE ALWAYS BEEN OUT ON A RAMPAGE DURING THE PARTY!

Haha YEP, THAT'S GREAT.

...

...

How nice!

WELL, YOU'RE HER BABYSITTER NOW, SO YOU CAN CELEBRATE WITH US!

YEAH, WHAT SHOULD I DO?

Wow YOU LOOK SO SERIOUS FOR ONCE...

WHAT ARE YOU GOING TO GET FOR HER PRESENT?

FLASH

112

LIKE, MAYBE YOU COULD DO SOMETHING NICE FOR HER...

THE MEMORY WOULD MAKE A GREAT PRESENT, RIGHT?

YOU DON'T HAVE TO THINK ABOUT IT TOO HARD.

Hrmm

LET'S SEE... WHAT WOULD MAKE HER HAPPY...?

HMM...

LIKE A HOME-COOKED MEAL...?

I SEE...

I DON'T THINK IT ALWAYS NEEDS TO BE SOMETHING PHYSICAL.

BUT I'VE NEVER COOKED ANYTHING BEFORE...

DON'T WORRY!

GRAB

clap

PERFECT! THAT'D MAKE FOR A GREAT MEMORY!

!

COOKING'S ALL ABOUT LOVE!

LOVE

LOVE, UH...

WHAM

ALL RIGHT, LET'S GET PRACTICING!

shff

SURE...

I'LL GET THE PAN READY. CAN YOU CUT THE VEGETABLES, TOORU-KUN?

SHAPE YOUR LEFT HAND INTO A CAT PAW SO YOU DON'T CUT YOUR FINGERS!

114

Whaaa?!

WHAT DID I JUST SAY?!

Yeesh...

GUSH

DISASTER

fwip

OH,

JUST POP THE CUT VEGGIES IN THIS...

HOW DOES THAT HAPPEN?!

Let's just get you cleaned up!!

It kinda turned into finger-cutting practice.

SORRY, I LOST TRACK OF WHETHER I WAS CUTTING CARROTS OR FINGERS...

Haha...

I WAS A LITTLE WORRIED AFTER THAT BLOOD-SOAKED CUTTING BOARD...

BUT I THINK YOU'RE STARTING TO GET THE HANG OF IT.

OKAY, WELL...

I JUST ASSOCIATE IT WITH CELEBRATING BIRTHDAYS, I GUESS.

I'M SURPRISED YOU SUGGESTED COOKING, THOUGH.

IS THERE A SPECIAL REASON FOR THAT?

TO ME, IT WAS THE BEST PRESENT OF ALL.

IT WAS NEVER ANYTHING FANCY, BUT...

Happy Birthday

THEN WE'LL HAVE TO MAKE SURE YAE-CHAN GETS YOUR BEST COOKING!

Haha

I'LL SEE WHAT I CAN DO.

It smells good, at least.

...

I SEE.

116

splat

I DID.

ALTHOUGH THE EGG'S NOT IN VERY GOOD SHAPE...

Ooooh...

YOU... MADE THIS, KIRI-SHIMA...?

CAN I EAT IT?

PLEASE DO!

HE PRAC-TICED...?

TOORU-KUN PRACTICED LOTS TO COOK FOR YOU, YAE-CHAN!

117

...TOORU...

Aaah

NAH...

I LIKE MY
BIRTHDAY
MEALS...

THE
BEST
PRES-
ENTS...

I'M
SORRY I CAN
NEVER BUY
PRESENTS
FOR YOU.

Pat

DON'T
ALWAYS
NEED TO BE
PHYSICAL.

Ah

KIRI-
SHIMA!

...MOM.

EXTRA

Ohh

WHAT DID YOU GET?

EVERYONE ELSE GAVE ME PRESENTS, TOO.

AND SUGIHARA GAVE ME LOTS OF COOL MII-CHAN STUFF.

They're all really rare!!

DADDY GAVE ME LOTS OF DRAWING STUFF.

rainbow⁺

RARE LIMITED-EDITION MERCH

SUPER-FANCY ART SUPPLIES

I'M SO GLAD I DIDN'T GO WITH A REGULAR GIFT!

I don't think I coulda compared to that...

WOW~

I'M GLAD TO HEAR IT~!

THANKS FOR THE FOOD

Chapter 23 Girl Talk

Parent-Teacher Association Meeting Room

chatter

THIS CONCLUDES TODAY'S PTA MEETING.

chatter

...HUH?

OH, UM, YEAH.

EXCUSE ME...

THIS WAS YOUR FIRST TIME HERE, RIGHT?

chatter

chatter

twitch

...UGHH...

OKAY, SAKURAGI-SAN?

IF YOU HAVE ANY QUESTIONS, PLEASE FEEL FREE TO ASK ♥

SQUEEE ♡

HERE ON YOUR WIFE'S BEHALF?

IT'S SO NICE OF A YOUNG MAN LIKE YOU TO SHOW UP!

MY HUSBAND COULD LEARN A THING OR TWO FROM YOU~!

GET ME THE HELL OUTTA HERE!

THANK YOU VERY MUCH!

smile ☆

KIRISHIMA... YOU STILL LOOK SO FUNNY.

Haha...

Pfft

THIS IS EMBAR-RASSING FOR ME, Y'KNOW...

sparkly~

Little lady!

SORRY TO KEEP YOU WAITING.

CAN WE GO GET DONUTS ON THE WAY HOME?

YES, OF COURSE!

Daddy gave me money 'cuz I'm in 2nd grade now.

Let's go!

YOU'RE RIGHT. SHOULD WE GET THOSE?

THEY GOT NEW DONUTS...!

KIRISHIMA!

NO WAY...

TOORU-CHAN...?

URGH...

I DIDN'T WANNA RUN INTO ANYONE RIGHT NOW, NEVER MIND YOU...!

What's with the getup? sooo cute!

Squeeee!

OMG, I WAS JUST ON MY WAY TO GO SEE YOU!

AH, SORRY, LITTLE GUY RIGHT AWAY...! I'LL GET RID OF THIS LADY!

Ah

LITTLE LADY...?

BLINK

AARGH AARGH

WHAT'RE YOU DOING HERE ANYWAY, HUH?

NO WAY IN HELL.

WE'RE GETTING THAT DRINK TONIGHT FOR SURE!

A boy...?
Or a girl...?

DAMMIT... I COULDN'T SHAKE HIM OFF...

I GUESS LIFE COMES AT YOU FAST...

Wooow...

munch

Whaaaaaat

YOU'RE BABYSITTING THE BOSS'S DAUGHTER?!

HEY. OVER HERE.

Don't talk to her.

Call me Rei-chan!

Rei-chan...

SO YOUR NAME'S YAEKA-CHAN, SWEETIE?

IF IT'S JUST ABOUT GETTING DRINKS, YOU CAN...

...SO, WHADDYA WANT WITH ME, ALREADY?

AND YOU KINDA TALK LIKE YOU'RE CLOSE FRIENDS...

YOU'RE ACTING FUNNY.

KIRISHIMA, IS REI-CHAN YOUR FRIEND?

HUH?

DISGUST

Yikes

AND WHAT IS THAT LOOK FOR?!

WE'RE CLOSER THAN AAANYONE EL...

Hee hee ♡

WE SURE ARE! WE'VE BEEN BESTIES SINCE MIDDLE SCHOOL.

Excuse me!

I SWEAR, YOU ARE SO RUDE TO ME!!

Uuuugggh

I CAN'T BELIEVE SHE GOT THE IDEA THAT I'M CLOSE WITH THIS BASTARD...

YAEKA-CHAN, HOW DOES TOORU-CHAN ACT WITH *YOU?*

NO ONE LIKES A SHY BOY, YOU KNOW.

YOU NEVER WERE ONE TO SHOW YOUR FEELINGS.

Hmph!

SHUT UP.

HE'S SMILEY AND NICE.

QUIT LOOKING SO GENUINELY CONFUSED, DAMMIT.

Now I'm pissed.

GRRRr

?

...?

FUNNY, THOSE'RE THE LAST WORDS I'D EVER PICK TO DESCRIBE YOU...

REALLY...?

YOU KNOW, THE OLD TOORU-CHAN HARDLY EVER SMILED, AND HIS EYES WERE ALWAYS SO COLD.

Smoking Room

UGHH...

* HAD TO TAKE A SMOKE BREAK

"TURNING POINT"...?

MM-HMM!

pat pat

BUT I GUESS BECOMING YOUR BABYSITTER MUST'VE BEEN THE TURNING POINT.

shff

I WAS WONDERING WHAT HAPPENED TO SOFTEN HIM UP...

YAEKA-CHAN...

IS A CHANGE THAT MAKES SOMEONE HAPPY.

A "TURNING POINT"

LOOK AFTER TOORU FOR ME, OKAY?

How rude.

WE WERE JUST HAVING A LITTLE GIRL TALK!

QUIET, YOU.

nod nod

LITTLE LADY...

PLEASE TELL ME HE BEHAVED HIMSELF.

I figured as much...

Hrm?

THAT ROUGH-AND-TUMBLE BOY WHO WAS ALWAYS PICKING A FIGHT WITH YOU.

MA-SAYA....?

YOU KNOW, RUNNING INTO YOU GOT ME THINKING...

DO YOU REMEMBER MASAYA?

MAN, I CAN'T WAIT TO KICK YOUR ASS...

THIS AIN'T NEARLY GOOD ENOUGH...

KIRISHIMA TOORU....!

WOW, THIS SUCKS.

UGH...

SO LET'S HANG OUT LIKE OLD TIMES ♥

That's what I came to tell you!

Oh, right

I JUST MOVED INTO THIS AREA RECENTLY,

I'LL GO GET A BAG, THEN.

That's nice.

I WANNA BRING BACK DONUTS FOR EVERYONE.

QUIVER

QUIVER

QUIVER

......

OH, WOW, I GET SOME TOO?

Yay!

THE CHOCOLATE'S FOR YOU, THE PLAIN'S FOR DADDY...

Strawberry for Sugihara...

OH DEAR, THE CONTRAST'S TOO CUTE TO HANDLE...

MMPH ....!

...THE HELL'RE YOU LOOKIN' AT? GET LOST.

GLARE

PFFFT

that I've never seen before~ ♥

I guess Tooru-chan still has charms

This is a story from before the little lady was born.

EXTRA

The Boss and His Wife

ONE PARTICULAR DAY, 8 YEARS AGO...

WHAT DID I TELL YOU, SIS?!

FWUMP

I SAID I WOULD TAKE CARE OF ALL THE CHORES UNTIL THE BABY'S BORN, DIDN'T I?!

Come on!

BOSS SAKURAGI'S SISTER-IN-LAW
KUROSAKI KANAMI (25)

JUST SIT DOWN AND REST ALREADY!

THWAM

Oh dear

C'MON~ YOU WORRY TOO MUCH~

shove

YOU'RE SPACY ENOUGH AS IT IS! WHAT IF YOU FELL DOWN?!

shove

SHE CHASED ME OUT...

Oops...

BOSS SAKURAGI'S WIFE
SAKURAGI MIYUKI (28)

GOOD MORNING, MA'AM!

OH~

AOI-KUN!

WHY ARE YOU STANDING AROUND OUT HERE?

BOSS SAKURAGI'S RIGHT-HAND MAN
AOI TOUICHIROU (27)

Ha ha ha

YEAH, YOU'RE ALWAYS ON THE MOVE.

She says I should rest...

I TRIED TO MAKE BREAKFAST, BUT KANAMI GOT MAD AT ME.

On that note...

ISN'T IT A BIT EARLY FOR YOU TO BE GOING OUT, AOI-KUN?

Ah

YEAH, ABOUT THAT...

I CAN'T BLAME HER FOR BEING NERVOUS WHEN SHE SEES THAT BELLY, THOUGH!

BUT I DON'T FEEL RIGHT JUST SITTING AROUND.

I WONDER IF HE'D COME BACK IF WE PUT SOME FOOD OUT FOR HIM?

I DUNNO, HE'S NOT A LOST CAT...

Maybe the smell would lure him back...

THAT DUMBASS TOORU HAS BEEN OUT RUNNING WILD FOR 3 DAYS NOW.

THOUGHT I'D TRACK HIM DOWN AND KICK HIS ASS!

OH DEAR, HOW AWFUL!

RRRUMBLE

Don't be too hard on him now~

AT THE END OF THE DAY, HE DOES LOOK OUT FOR TOORU-KUN.

BUT YOU AND THE LITTLE ONE SHOULD JUST TAKE IT EASY, MA'AM!

......

WHAT'RE YOU DOING THERE?

BOSS OF THE SAKURAGI FAMILY
SAKURAGI KAZUHIKO (37)

RATTLE

OH, DEAR.

YOU CAUGHT ME ALREADY?

MIYUKI.

I knew I felt someone watching me...

WOULD YOU MIND INDULGING ME?

BUT IT'S BORING HAVING NOTHING TO DO.

...SURE.

EVERYONE'S TRYING TO HELP BY TELLING ME TO RELAX...

AW, A SAKURA PATTERN!

WHAT WERE YOU LOOKING AT SO INTENTLY?

ONE OF THE RICE BOWLS I USED TO COLLECT.

FOR ONCE OUR CHILD'S OLD ENOUGH TO EAT SOLID FOOD.

I FIGURED THIS KIND OF THING MIGHT BE USEFUL...

I WOULDN'T EXPECT YOU TO PICK SOMETHING SO CUTE, KAZUHIKO-SAN.

SINCE YOU'RE THE ONE WHO PICKED IT OUT!

...I'M SURE THE BABY WILL LOVE IT.

ALTHOUGH THAT WON'T BE FOR A WHILE...

hee

hee

...?

WHAT IS IT?

...I SURE HOPE SO.

I WAS JUST WONDERING WHICH OF US THE BABY'S GOING TO TAKE AFTER?

IF IT'S ME, I'M SURE WE'LL HAVE CHATTERBOX ON OUR HANDS.

WOULDN'T THAT...

COME FROM YOU, TOO?

......

Whaaat~?

NO, IT'S YOU!

AND IF IT'S YOU...

THEN OUR CHILD WILL GROW UP KIND AND STRONG.

Awwww~

THIS IS THE CUTEST CONVERSATION EVER~!!

SHFF

...HEY, YOU TWO!

BREAKFAST IS...

KNOWING THESE TWO, I'M SURE THEIR BABY

IS GONNA BE SUPER HAPPY.

DASH

WHAT'S WRONG?!

SORRY, DIDN'T MEAN TO SCARE YA...

...AH!

KANAMI?!

EEEEEEEEEEK?!!

...HEY, IT SCARED ME TOO.

DON'T SCARE ME LIKE THAT, TOORU-KUN~!!

rustle

SAKURAGI FAMILY UP-AND-COMER KIRISHIMA TOORU (20)

MAYBE HE REALLY IS A LOST CAT...!!

Wha...

BUT I GOT HUNGRY, SO I CAME HOME.

That's all...

Yikes... I DUNNO... OUT?

Brace yourself, punk!

WHERE THE HELL HAVE YOU BEEN, YOU DAMN MORON?!

GRAB

Hee hee

WELL, I THINK IT'S FUN!

Sigh...

...NOISY BASTARDS, AREN'T THEY?

Whatever, I'm gonna kick your ass now!

Wait, why...?

Ow ow ow

IT'S ONE BIG "FAMILY" OF PEOPLE WHO ADMIRE YOU.

I LOVE EVERY LAST ONE OF THEM.

THANK YOU SO, SO MUCH...!

So cool...!

Well, how about that.

snifffffle

CV: Watada Misaki-san

CV: Hosoya Yoshimasa-san

HOSOYA YOSHIMASA-SAN (KIRISHIMA) AND WATADA MISAKI-SAN (YAEKA) REALLY BROUGHT THE CHARACTERS TO LIFE.

AND I WAS LUCKY ENOUGH TO HAVE LOTS OF MERCHANDISE MADE TO COME OUT WITH THIS VOLUME. I HOPE YOU LIKE IT!

I have a habit of drawing → these sorts of faces

She's cute, I like her

I drew lots of new art for them!

I HAD FUN FOCUSING ON DIFFERENT CHARACTERS AND INTRODUCING NEW ONES IN VOLUME 2.

I HOPE WE CAN MEET AGAIN IN THE NEXT VOLUME!

I also read

all my fan letter

THANK YOU ALL FOR SHARING YOUR THOUGHTS AND COMMENTS IN VARIOUS WAYS.

UNLESS I'M SORELY MISTAKEN...

THE ENEMY LEADER IS SOMEONE VERY CLOSE TO YOU, YAEKA...

STOP DOING EVIL STUFF!

It's you...!!

MAGICAL GIRL YAEKA!!

dun

dun

KIRISHIM

DON'T TELL ME...

THAT'S QUITE A SCARY FACE...

...WHAT'S THE MATTER?

144

145

The Yakuza's Guide to Babysitting
Author: Tsukiya   VOL. 2

KUMICHOMUSUME TO SEWAGAKARI VOL. 2 by Tsukiya
© 2019 Tsukiya
© MICRO MAGAZINE
All rights reserved.
Original Japanese edition published in 2019 by MICRO MAGAZINE, INC.
English translation rights granted by MICRO MAGAZINE, INC.

For press inquiries or review copies, please send all correspondence to info@kaitenbooks.com

Kaiten Books and the Kaiten Books logo are copyright of Kaiten Books, LLC. All rights reserved

ISBNs: 978-1-952241-25-3 (paperback)
978-1-952241-24-6 (ebook)
Printed in Canada
First Printing: 2021

Translation:
Jenny McKeon

Editing:
David Musto

Typesetting:
Viet Phuong Vu

Quality Assurance:
B. Lillian Martin

Cover Design:
Kazushi Mizutani

Production Manager:
Garrison Denim

Brand Manager:
Christian Knoll

I.T. Administrator:
Brandon Cao

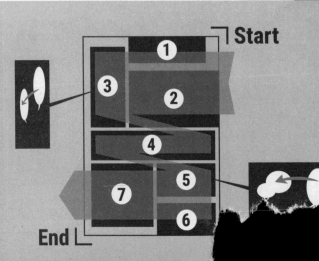

Reading Instructions:

Each page reads from *right to left*; starting from the top right, ending at bottom left. Simple as that. Follow diagram on left.

Come visit us online ... ooks.com